TRANSFORMERS PRIME

OFFICIAL HANDBOOK

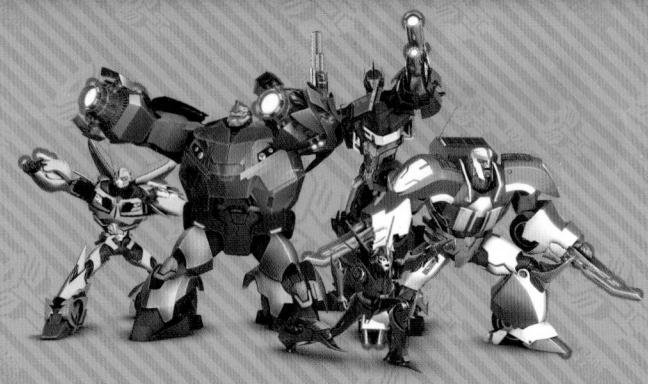

TRANSFORMERS PRIME: OFFICIAL HANDBOOK
A BANTAM BOOK 978 0 857 51112 6

First published in Great Britain by Bantam
an imprint of Random House Children's Books
A Random House Group Company

This edition published 2012

1 3 5 7 9 10 8 6 4 2

Bantam Books are published by Random House Children's Books,
61–63 Uxbridge Road, London W5 5SA

www.kidsatrandomhouse.co.uk
www.totallyrandombooks.co.uk

Addresses for companies within The Random House Group Limited
can be found at: www.randomhouse.co.uk/offices.htm

THE RANDOM HOUSE GROUP Limited Reg. No. 954009

A CIP catalogue record for this book is available from the British Library.

Printed in Italy

CONTENTS

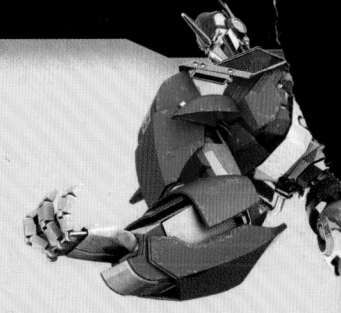

DARKNESS RISING

Meet Optimus Prime and his team of Autobots. Team Prime's sworn mission is to defend planet Earth from the evil Decepticons and protect the safety of all humankind.

The Decepticons are back with a vengeance, under the command of the powerful Megatron. They will not rest until the universe is theirs to control.

Megatron has discovered a rare element known as Dark Energon, and he's ready to use it to raise an army.

An undead army that can't be defeated . . .

Or can it?

And the story continues . . .

5

OPTIMUS PRIME

PROFILE **AUTOBOT**

The leader of the Autobots is the largest, strongest and wisest of Team Prime. He feels responsible for the protection of each human in the Autobots' war against the Decepticons.

As Autobot commander he carries the weight of both Cybertron and Earth on his shoulders. Optimus has seen many battles and he knows there are more to come. As a 'Prime' he is part of an incredible legacy, one that is unfolding to this day . . .

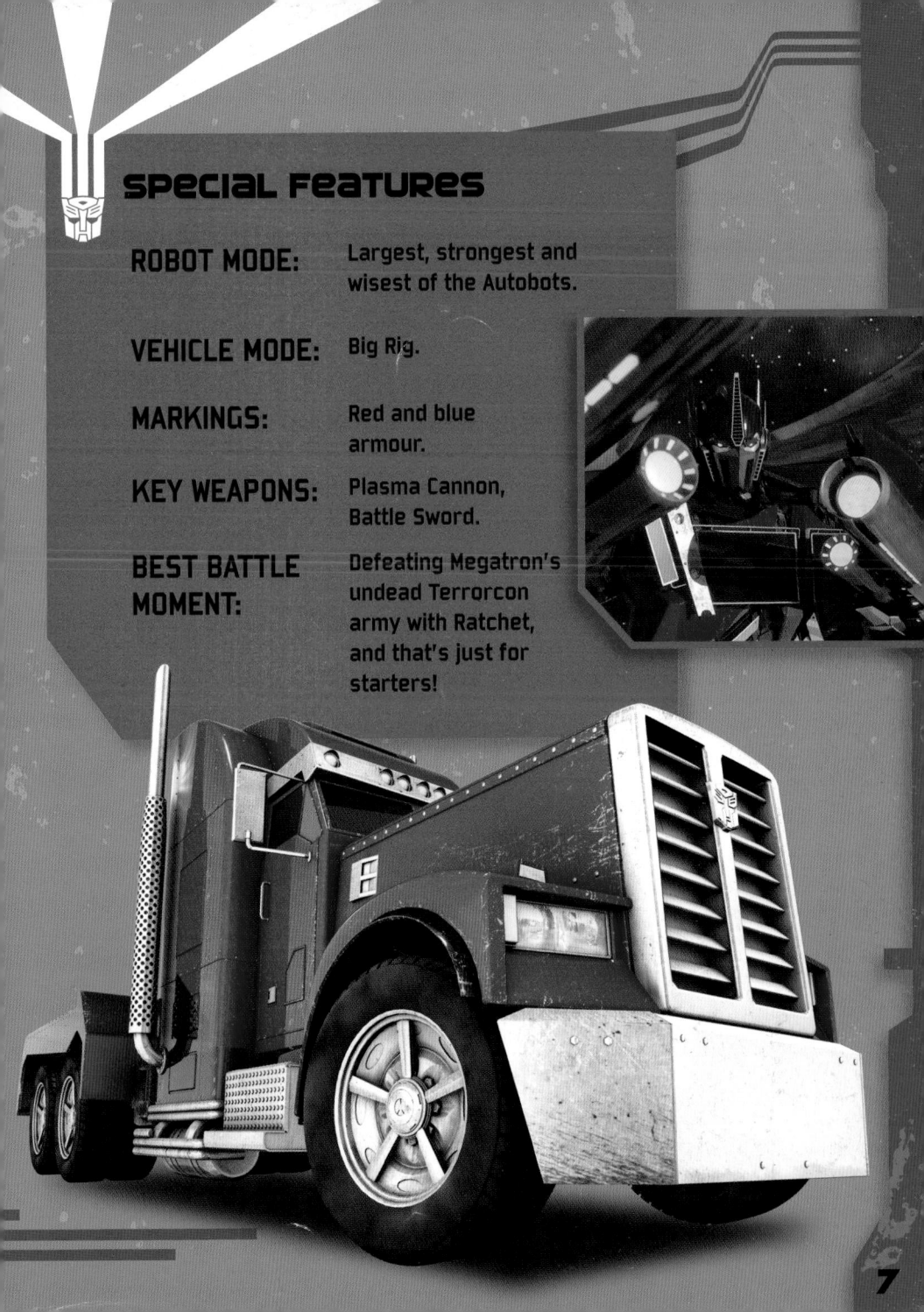

SPECIAL FEATURES

ROBOT MODE: Largest, strongest and wisest of the Autobots.

VEHICLE MODE: Big Rig.

MARKINGS: Red and blue armour.

KEY WEAPONS: Plasma Cannon, Battle Sword.

BEST BATTLE MOMENT: Defeating Megatron's undead Terrorcon army with Ratchet, and that's just for starters!

ENERGON VS

Energon is the fuel and life-blood of the Autobots and the Decepticons.

The Autobots' home planet of Cybertron is uninhabitable, ravaged by centuries of civil war between the Autobots and the Decepticons.

During the Great War on Cybertron, both sides hid Energon supplies on other planets.

Now the Decepticons have brought the battle to Earth, a planet which has one of the greatest hidden Energon deposits in the universe.

When a Bot or Con is injured they lose Energon. If they are badly injured and lose a large amount of Energon, their life signal is at risk.

'You will not prevail Megatron. Not while Energon flows through my veins.'

DARK ENERGON

Dark Energon is the antithesis of Energon. Legend tells that it has the power to revive the dead. Ancient texts refer to Unicron the Destroyer whose blood was the anti-Spark.
It turns fallen warriors into 'Zombified' Terrorcons. Their only instinct is to destroy everything in their path.

When Bots are awoken with Dark Energon they are no longer Bots but 'Terrorcons', essentially robot zombies. They must be commanded by a higher being using Dark Energon to control them, or they will mindlessly crush everything in their path.

AUTOBOT RULES

Unlike the Decepticons, Autobots have a deep respect for any kind of life. They've seen what civil war did to their home planet of Cybertron, and it is their sworn duty to protect Earth from a similar fate.

AUTOBOT RULES

RULE 1: Keep a low profile

RULE 2: Any human who learns about the Autobots has to be protected

RULE 3: Never abuse power for personal gain

Only a few individuals on Earth know about the existence of the Autobots, and the location of their secret base Autobot Outpost Omega One. The Autobots will stop at nothing to protect them from the Decepticons.

RATCHET

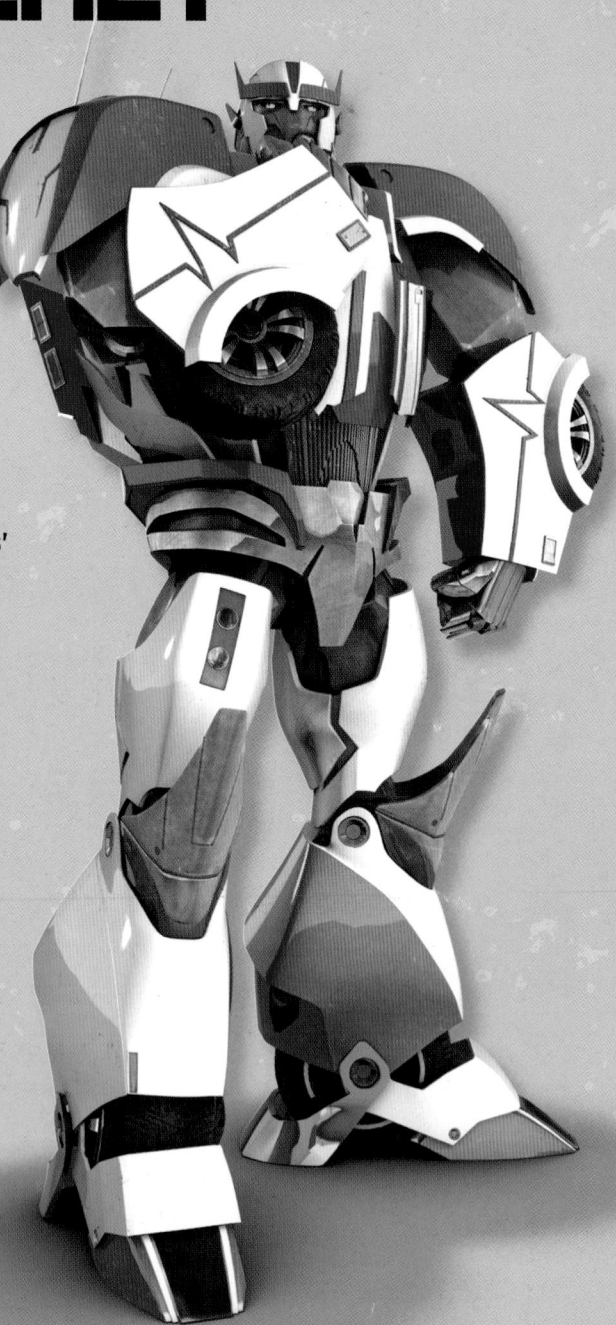

This emergency medical truck is the Autobots' medic. Engineer, scientist and all-round 'Doc Bot', he repairs busted limbs and gears when needed, designs weapons and technology and brainstorms ways of improving the Autobots' dwindling Energon supplies.

He's reluctant for the Autobots to risk their necks protecting humans, but more and more, Ratchet admires what their new allies can bring to the fight.

'DID YOU MISS US, DOC BOT?'

SPECIAL FEATURES

ROBOT MODE: Autobot Medic.

VEHICLE MODE: Hybrid Emergency Medical Vehicle.

MARKINGS: Red and white armour.

KEY WEAPON: Dynametal Scalpel.

BEST BATTLE MOMENT: Ratchet's invention of the GroundBridge, a device that can transport the Autobots anywhere on Earth.

AUTOBOT HQ

INSIDE THE SILO

Autobot Outpost Omega One is a former missile silo, and ideal for the Autobots to use as their HQ. Hidden out of sight in the Nevada desert, its location is a secret sought after by the Decepticons.

Of all the Autobots, Ratchet operates most of the HQ and makes more modifications as the Autobots need. He runs the sickbay and uses his equipment to run diagnostics, examine specimens and help fix the other Bots.

Ratchet's amazing GroundBridge is operated from here. Wherever any of Team Prime are in the world, they can always be transported back to HQ via the GroundBridge. The silo walls block all radiowaves, making it a safe haven where the Autobots can refuel on Energon and plan their next moves.

The humans – Raf, Jack and Miko love the base as well. They can chill out with their Bots and learn more about Cybertronian ways – so much more interesting than homework!

One of the only other humans who knows the location of the base and can come and go as he pleases is Special Agent Fowler – he frequently pays a visit to shout at Optimus!

DARKNESS RISING CONTINUED . . .

Megatron needs an unlimited supply of fallen robots to make into Terrorcons using Dark Energon. Where could he find so many? CYBERTRON!

If Megatron can transport the Terrorcons from Cybertron to Earth no-one will survive. It's time for Optimus to act.

If the Decepticons can lock the coordinates of their Spacebridge onto Cybertron, the Terrorcons can be transported to Earth. But the Autobots have help from an unexpected source . . .

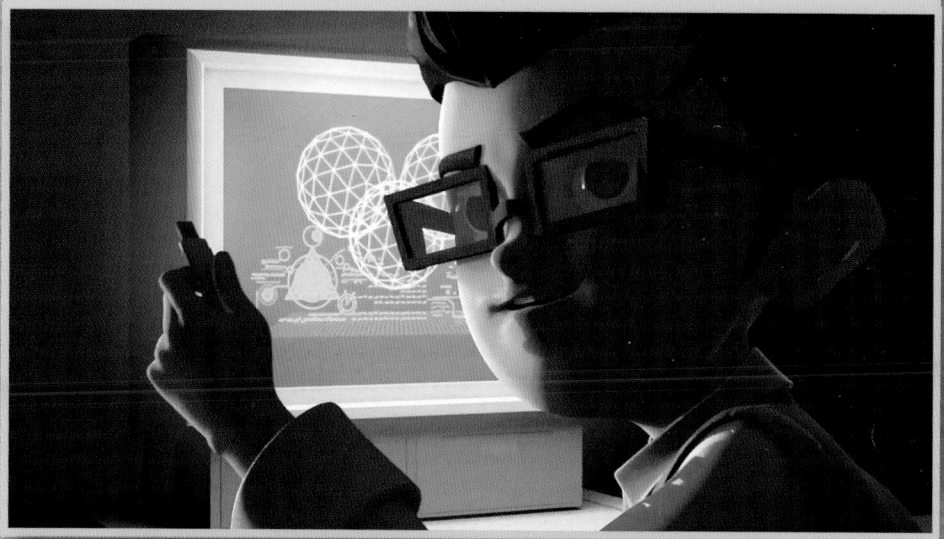

But despite Raf's help, the Decepticons lock on and prepare to transport the Terrorcons . . .

And the story continues . . .

STEALTHY CHARACTERS

Can you match these Decepticons to their shadows?
Watch out! They're slippery customers and liable to trick you!

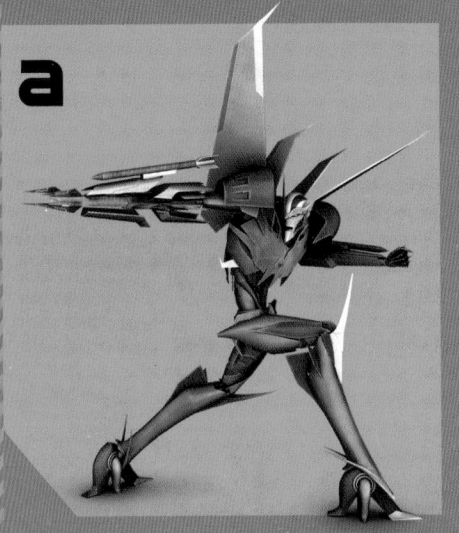

a

B

C

a

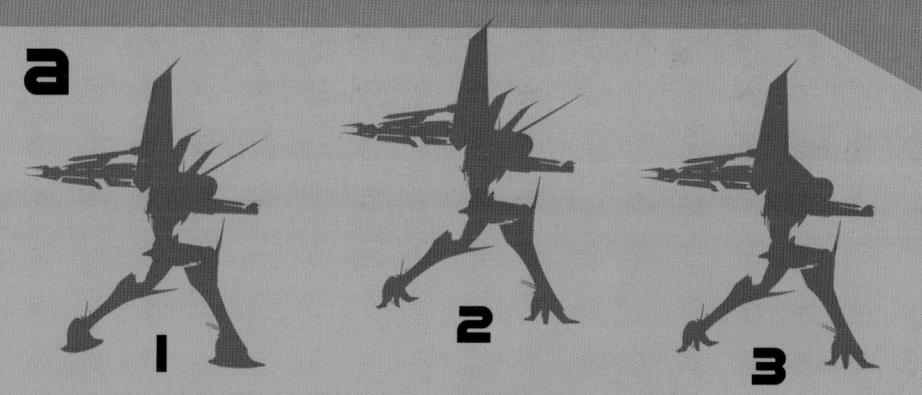

1

2

3

B

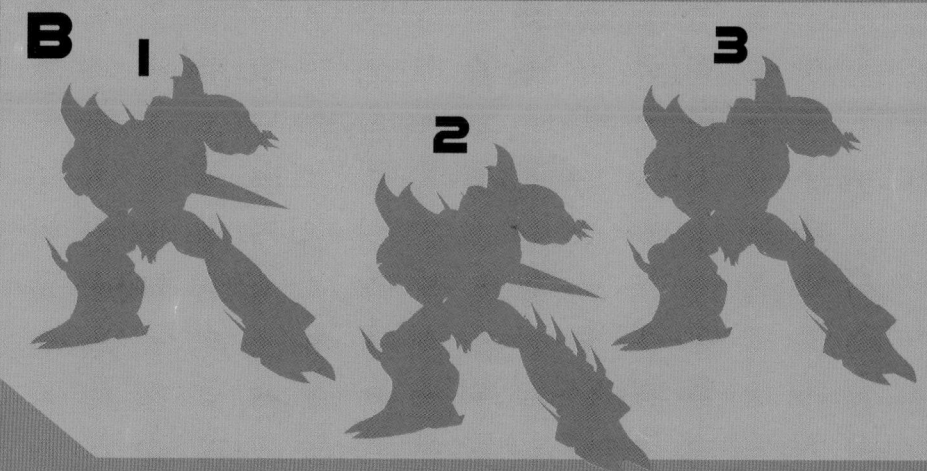

1

2

3

C

1

2

3

Answers on page 96

BUMBLEBEE

He's a tough muscle car, and also the Autobot who's been on Earth the longest. He knows humans the best, and takes the responsibility of protecting Raf very seriously.

His voicebox was damaged on Cybertron and he speaks in a variety of bleeps and blurts.

SPECIAL FEATURES

ROBOT MODE: Large by human standards, but one of the most compact of the Autobots.

VEHICLE MODE: Muscle car.

MARKINGS: Yellow and black armour.

KEY WEAPON: Stingers.

BEST BATTLE MOMENT: Saving Optimus from the Cybonic Plague.

AUTOBOT

PROFILE

The youngest
Autobot on Team
Prime, Bumblebee
has a tendency
to act without
thinking, but he is
loyal, brave and
always ready to
defend others,
even against
impossible odds.

Bumblebee's
finest hour comes
when he gets the
formula to save
Optimus from the
Cybonic Plague.
Unfortunately, it

also turns into his weakest, when it is revealed that Megatron has
taken Bumblebee over and intends to bend him to his evil ends.
Thankfully Bumblebee survives the ordeal unscathed.

DECEPTICON ALERT!

A Decepticon has managed to hide amongst the Autobots!
Can you find him before he starts any trouble?

Answers
on page 96

ENERGON CRISIS!

The Autobots are running low on Energon. Can you help them find some more? Show Arcee which way to go by following the word Energon as it appears below. It's crunch time!

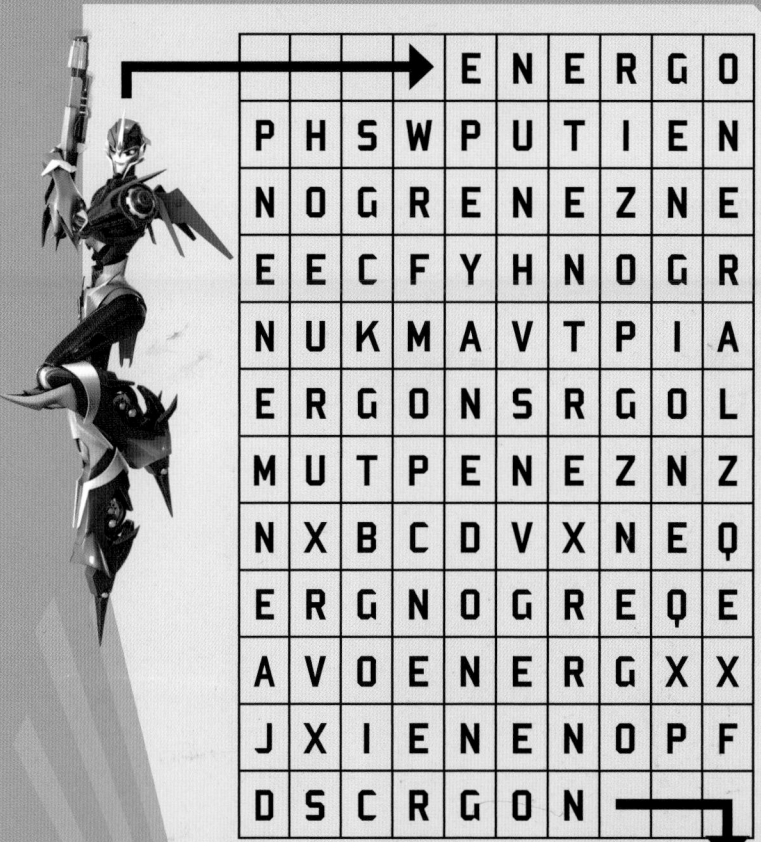

				E	N	E	R	G	O
P	H	S	W	P	U	T	I	E	N
N	O	G	R	E	N	E	Z	N	E
E	E	C	F	Y	H	N	O	G	R
N	U	K	M	A	V	T	P	I	A
E	R	G	O	N	S	R	G	O	L
M	U	T	P	E	N	E	Z	N	Z
N	X	B	C	D	V	X	N	E	Q
E	R	G	N	O	G	R	E	Q	E
A	V	O	E	N	E	R	G	X	X
J	X	I	E	N	E	N	O	P	F
D	S	C	R	G	O	N			

arcee

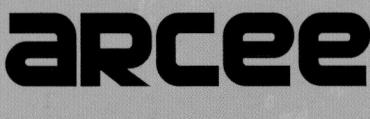

'PUT THE METAL TO THE PEDAL!'

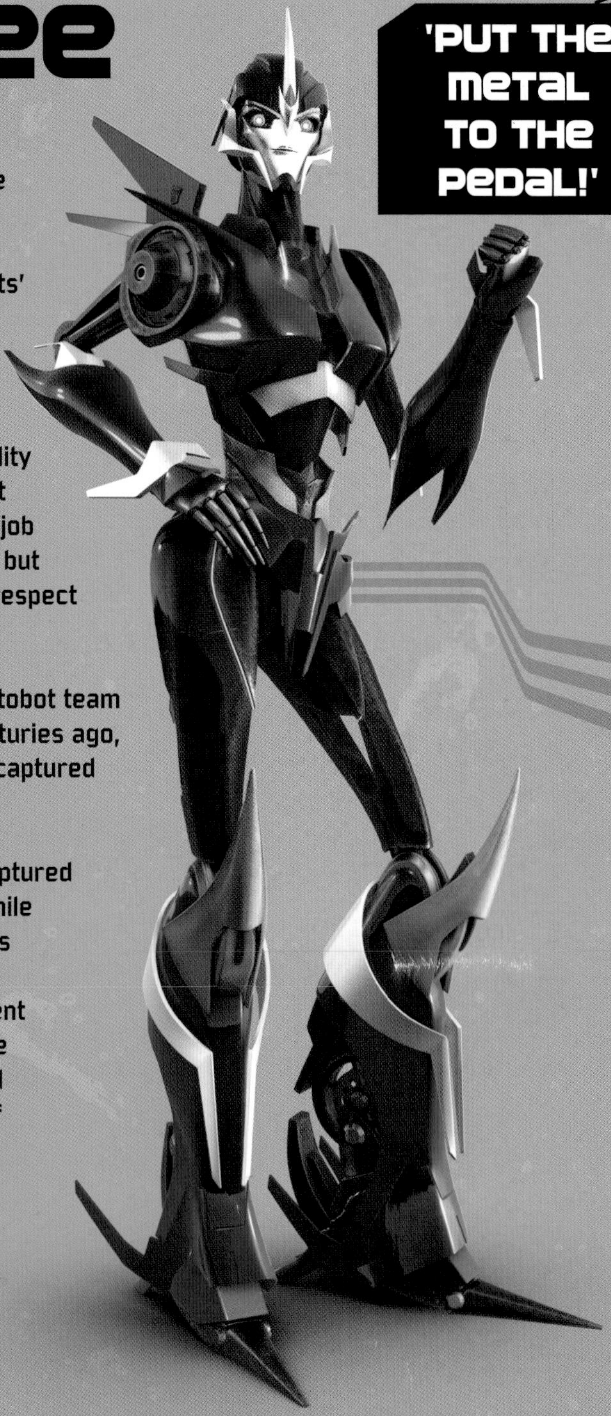

Arcee is one awesome motorcycle – sleek, fast, and powerful. She's also the Autobots' best soldier. Not as strong as the other Bots maybe, but what she lacks in muscle she has in agility and speed. She wasn't too thrilled to get the job of looking after Jack, but she slowly comes to respect him as a partner.

Arcee has lost two Autobot team members before. Centuries ago, Autobot Tailgate was captured by Airachnid.

Then Cliffjumper is captured by the Decepticons while out on patrol. When his spark shows back up online Arcee is adamant that they have to save him. When she's faced with the awful truth of his reawakening with Dark Energon she can't bear it.

PROFILE AUTOBOT

SPECIAL FEATURES

ROBOT MODE: Sleek and nimble, yet a powerful warrior.

VEHICLE MODE: Motorcycle.

MARKINGS: Blue, black and silver armour.

KEY WEAPON: Twin Ion Blasters.

BEST BATTLE MOMENT: Blowing up the Decepticon Spacebridge!

WHO'S OUT OF THE FRAME?

Can you work out which of the missing pieces will complete the picture?

a

C

D

B

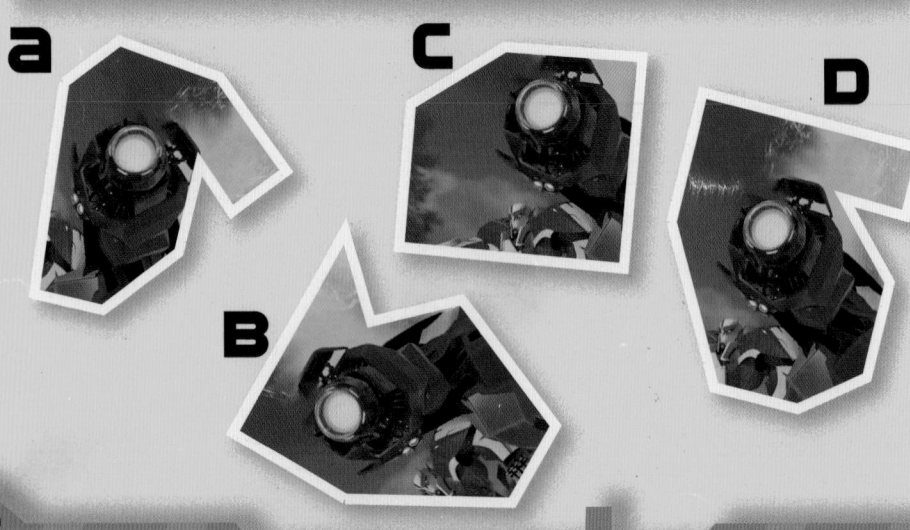

SPACE EQUATION

Can you help Ratchet work out this puzzle and decipher Megatron's plan?

×	%	÷	:	*	&	...	?	ẫ	[	^	;	o
A	B	C	D	E	F	G	H	I	J	K	L	M

ø	§	±	]	▪	¶	=	!	✝	|	_	«	»
N	O	P	Q	R	S	T	U	V	W	X	Y	Z

¶	±	×	÷	*	%	▪	ẫ	:	...	*		=	§

÷	«	%	*	▪	=	▪	§	ø

Answers on page 96

BULKHEAD

Massive Bulkhead is the muscle of the Autobots! He embodies terrific strength and often gives the Autobots the edge in their fight against the Decepticons. He's keenly aware of the 'fragility' of humans, particularly in relation to his massive form, and he's paranoid about hurting his human companion, Miko.

SPECIAL FEATURES

ROBOT MODE: The muscle of the Autobots.

VEHICLE MODE: All-Terrain Vehicle.

MARKINGS: Khaki green armour.

KEY WEAPON: Forestonite Battle Mace.

BEST BATTLE MOMENT: Realising that the Decepticon Shapeshifter is disguised as his old friend Wheeljack.

Bulkhead has a big heart to match his huge frame and embraces humans into his world. He may not be the sharpest of the Autobots but when faced with a Decepticon disguised as an old friend, he soon begins to realize that something is wrong. He is not to be underestimated!

TRUE OR FALSE?

1 Optimus Prime and Megatron once fought side by side.

2 All Decepticons use a flying machine as their vehicle mode.

3 Arcee is the smallest of the Autobots.

4 The Autobots can live without Energon.

5 Bulkhead's vehicle mode is a motorbike.

WORD GAME

No-one can hear a word Optimus is saying over the din of Miko and her band practicing. He's trying to give an order to the Autobots, can you work out what it is? Add a letter to the middle column of each line so that it forms a word on each side.

ROA _ IDE

SIL _ PEN

WAL _ EAD

HIL _ OOK

ALS _ VER

YO _ NIT

TEN _ HAT

Answers on page 96

CLIFFJUMPER

This adventurous robot loves to patrol and is always up for some fun, but when he stumbles upon the Decepticon ship Nemesis and a sinkhole full of Energon, he needs backup fast.

> **'FAIR WARNING, I'LL PUT A FEW DINGS IN YA'**

SPECIAL FEATURES

ROBOT MODE: Adventurous Bot who never backs down from a fight.

VEHICLE MODE: Red muscle car.

MARKINGS: Red and silver armour.

BEST BATTLE MOMENT: Taking on the might of the Decepticon Troopers.

PROFILE

Unfortunately he doesn't make it, and is dragged to
Starscream who extinguishes his spark. When Megatron
needs a Bot to try out the effects of Dark Energon,
Cliffjumper is re-awakened. But he is not Cliffjumper.
He is a Terrorcon, an uncontrollable destroyer.

DARKNESS RISING CONTINUED . . .

The only hope the Autobots have is to blow up the Spacebridge.

Ratchet can tell them how from HQ.

But Megatron won't let it happen without a fight, so one of the Autobots will have to act as a decoy and distract him.

It's an epic battle . . . As Optimus and Megatron fight, Arcee turns the flow of Energon around. The Spacebridge implodes, stopping the Terrorcons in their tracks.

Optimus escapes just in time, to see the Bridge explode, seemingly destroying Megatron . . .

THE END

MEGATRON

This age-old robot is the leader of the Decepticons, and the most sinister and deadly of all the Transformers.

'ALL HAIL MEGATRON!'

SPECIAL FEATURES

ROBOT MODE: Equal to Optimus Prime in size.

VEHICLE MODE: Alien fighter jet.

MARKINGS: Black and silver armour.

KEY WEAPON: Fusion Cannon.

BEST BATTLE MOMENT: Rising again from the Spacebridge explosion and leading the Decepticons once more.

Whether in alien fighter form or robot mode, he is highly skilled with a deadly arsenal of weapons. A ruthless warrior who shows no mercy, Megatron is obsessed with defeating Optimus Prime and watches in disgust as his opponent tries to protect the pathetic humans that run rampant over planet Earth.

Starscream may be desperate to overthrow him, but Megatron is held in fear and awe by all, so Starscream is careful not to show his longing too clearly.

INSIDE NEMESIS

THE DECEPTICON HQ

Nemesis is the Decepticon mobile headquarters and it gives them a supreme advantage over the Bots by being able to land wherever they want, along with their army of Troopers and high-tech equipment.

NEMESIS SPECIAL FEATURES

- Capacity to transport thousands of troops.
- Vast array of high-spec technical equipment.
- Drilling equipment and storage for huge amounts of Energon.
- Ability to power a Spacebridge for intergalactic travel.
- Limited stealth ability. Being so big, Nemesis can't land just anywhere and remain unnoticed. Although the Decepticons don't really mind crushing whoever gets in their path.

AUTOBOT FIT

See if you can fit the Autobots into the spaces below.

ARCEE

BUMBLEBEE

BULKHEAD

RATCHET

OPTIMUS

STARSCREAM

This military fighter jet is Megatron's right hand Con. He is a fearsome opponent who prefers sneak attacks over direct confrontation. Ambush is his speciality, whether from the sky, underground or in disguise. Starscream is truly the most 'deceptive' of all the Decepticons.

SPECIAL FEATURES

ROBOT MODE: Smaller than Megatron although monstrous and deadly to all humans and most Autobots.

VEHICLE MODE: Military fighter jet.

MARKINGS: Black armour with red markings.

KEY WEAPON: Null Missiles.

BEST BATTLE MOMENT: Obtaining the powerful lens to mine for Energon in the Arctic.

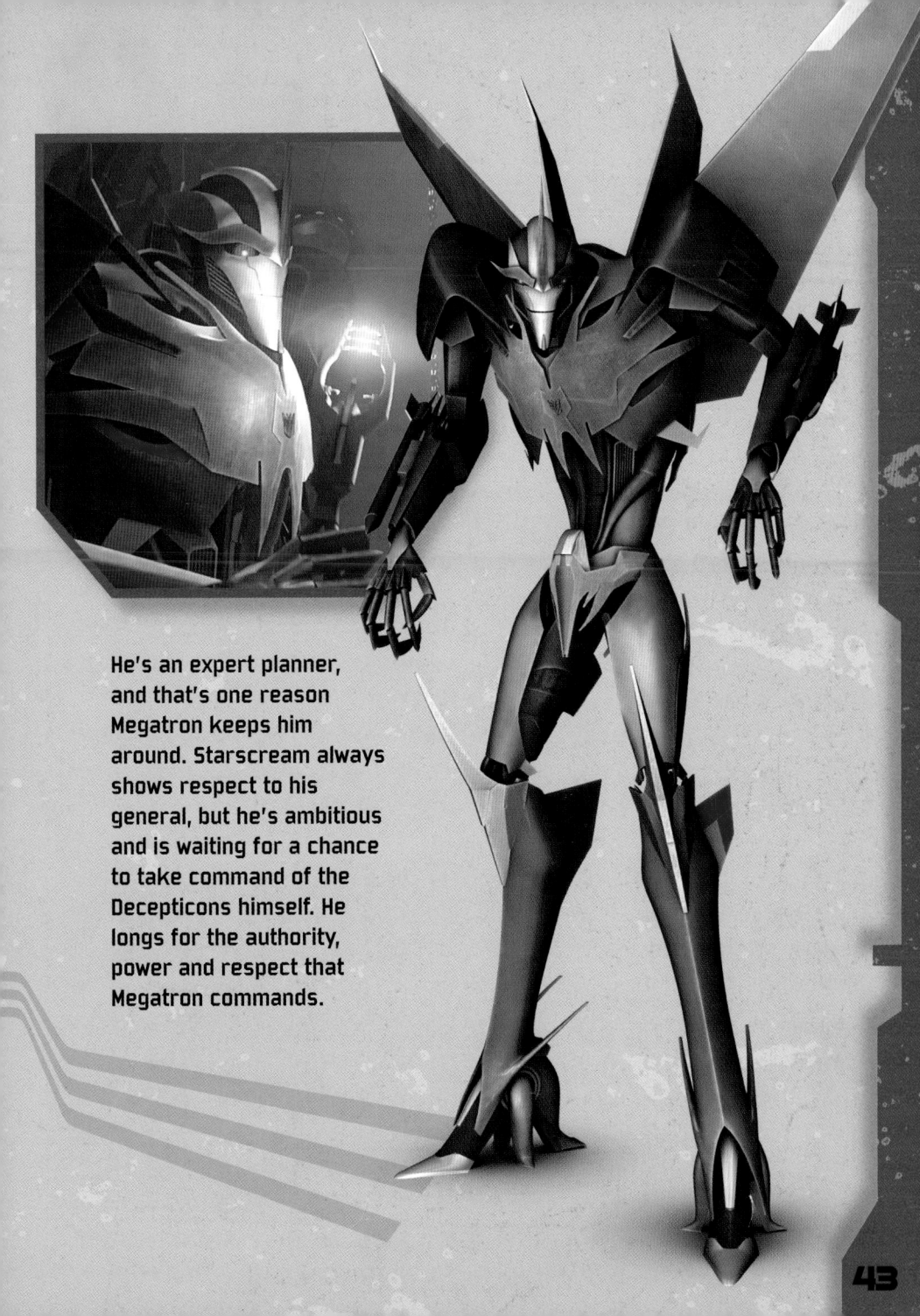

He's an expert planner, and that's one reason Megatron keeps him around. Starscream always shows respect to his general, but he's ambitious and is waiting for a chance to take command of the Decepticons himself. He longs for the authority, power and respect that Megatron commands.

WHO'S THIS?

Can you match the description to the character?

1 A gentle giant who has a habit of breaking things. He is the muscle of the group and has a big heart.

RAF

2 This robot has seen decades of civil war on his beloved Cybertron and now fears that the same could happen on planet Earth. He will stop at nothing to prevent this happening.

STARSCREAM

3 A quick thinker and speedy in her actions, too. She can be a bit snappy to humans but she enjoys their company more than she will admit.

BULKHEAD

4

A slippery customer who would love to cut out his boss and rule the skies. This robot is a true Decepticon!

SOUNDWAVE

5

He didn't want to join with the Autobots, he thought it would bring trouble and danger. But as his friendship with Arcee grows he finds himself at the HQ more and more.

OPTIMUS PRIME

6

A hacker, computer whiz and he's only 12! The youngest human in the group yet more than once he's saved everybody with his computer skills.

ARCEE

7

Silent yet deadly. This Decepticon listens and takes in everything over the airwaves.

JACK

Answers on page 96

BY THE ALLSPARK

With Megatron out of action, the Decepticons are being led by Starscream.

When Breakdown finds a mural of an Energon Harvester in Greece, it is recognized by the Decepticons straight away.

But it is also recognized by the Autobots. And thanks to Raf they know exactly where to find it – in a museum!

The race is on to find the Harvester!

And the story continues . . .

SOUNDWAVE

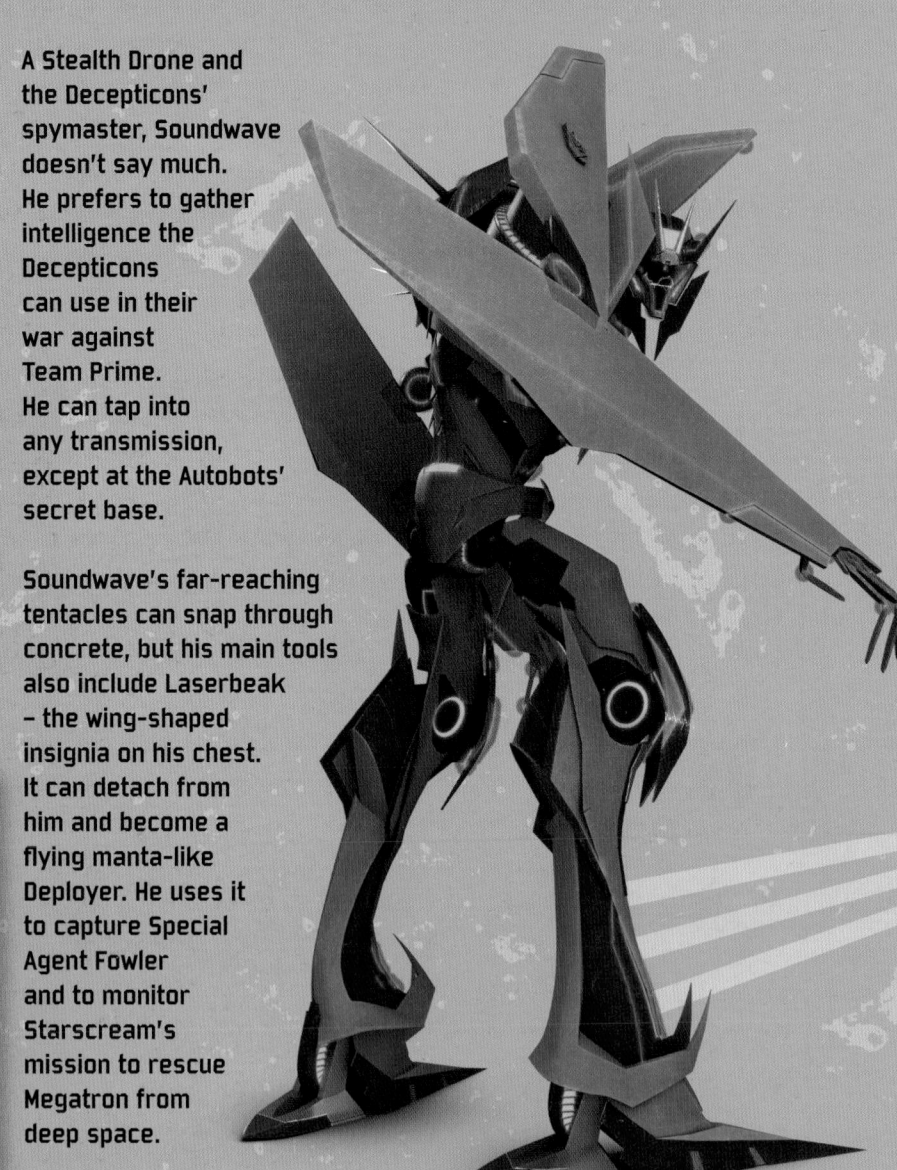

A Stealth Drone and the Decepticons' spymaster, Soundwave doesn't say much. He prefers to gather intelligence the Decepticons can use in their war against Team Prime. He can tap into any transmission, except at the Autobots' secret base.

Soundwave's far-reaching tentacles can snap through concrete, but his main tools also include Laserbeak – the wing-shaped insignia on his chest. It can detach from him and become a flying manta-like Deployer. He uses it to capture Special Agent Fowler and to monitor Starscream's mission to rescue Megatron from deep space.

SPECIAL FEATURES

ROBOT MODE: Faceless and silent, reflecting his role as master of espionage.

VEHICLE MODE: Stealth Drone.

MARKINGS: Black armour with blue and purple streaks.

KEY WEAPON: Nucleon Tentacle Flails.

BEST BATTLE MOMENT: Sending Laserbeak to monitor Starscream's mission to rescue Megatron. Otherwise Starscream would have finished Megatron off.

WHEELJACK VS MAKESHIFT

Wheeljack is an Autobot who prefers to travel alone, hunting for adventures and living by his wheels. He is an old friend of Bulkhead's from the Great War when they fought in the same 'Wreckers' warrior unit.

Makeshift is a Decepticon who can change himself into any other robot he wishes. At the request of Starscream he becomes Wheeljack and manoeuvres his way into the Autobots' HQ.

AUTOBOT

PROFILE

WHEELJACK
SPECIAL FEATURES

ROBOT MODE: A warrior Bot who travels the galaxy, hunting for adventures.

VEHICLE MODE: Wheeljack only spent a short time on Earth, his vehicle mode is yet to be chosen.

MARKINGS: Red, white and green armour.

KEY WEAPON: Two swords attached to his back that he uses like a cyber-samurai.

BEST BATTLE MOMENT: Escaping from Nemesis, beating Makeshift and sending him back to the Decepticons with a bang!

But Wheeljack is not to be underestimated and manages to free himself and make it to the Autobot base where he battles Makeshift. Wheeljack sends him back to the Decepticons via the GroundBridge with a 'goodbye' present, a detonated grenade attached to him.

KNOCKOUT & BREAKDOWN

Knockout is the Decepticon medic and Breakdown is his trusty sidekick and assistant. They first become known to the Autobots when they find them in Greece looking at the mural of the Energon Harvester.

Knockout can't resist a good race with humans to show his superiority, but he gets his smooth finish scraped when he comes to blows with Bumblebee.

DECEPTICON

PROFILE

KNOCKOUT
SPECIAL FEATURES

ROBOT MODE: Decepticon medic.

VEHICLE MODE: Cool car.

MARKINGS: Red and silver armour, with yellow markings.

BEST BATTLE MOMENT: Joining with Starscream to oust Megatron.

> 'YOU SCRATCH MY PAINT, I'LL SCRATCH YOURS.'

Knockout is slightly distrusted by Starscream because of his choice of a ground vehicle rather than a flying one, but he comes to see him as his greatest ally once Knockout panders to his need for power. Together they scheme and Knockout is promised the Number Two position, only to be thwarted when Megatron returns, stronger than ever.

BREAKDOWN
SPECIAL FEATURES

ROBOT MODE: Decepticon muscle.

VEHICLE MODE: Breakdown truck.

MARKINGS: Silver and black armour.

BEST BATTLE MOMENT: Teaming up with Bulkhead to escape from MECH. Even if it was only so that they could have a re-match battle later!

AIRACHNID

This is one scary Con! Airachnid is a loner and takes no prisoners. A former ally of Megatron, she once preferred to travel the galaxy, collecting the heads of her victims and placing them on the walls of her spaceship. Until she met Megatron again, and realized that the number two spot was wide open for the taking.

SPECIAL FEATURES

ROBOT MODE: Spider with six arms and two legs.

VEHICLE MODE: Helicopter.

MARKINGS: Black armour.

BEST BATTLE MOMENT: Ousting Starscream to become Megatron's number two commander.

PROFILE   DECEPTICON

'WE MEET AGAIN, ARCEE.'

She's a spider-like robot with six arms and two legs and is a formidable opponent. Her history with Arcee means that when Arcee sees her, she starts having terrible flashbacks of Airachnid capturing her and her former partner, Tailgate.

When Airachnid decides that she will add Jack's scalp to her collection, Arcee feels powerless to do anything to stop her. However through sheer fury and a need to protect Jack, Arcee manages to overcome her fears and face Airachnid once again. Defeated Airachnid drills into the ground and escapes through a tunnel.

A short-lived union with MECH and Silas didn't have the outcome she had hoped for, and she still didn't manage to finish Arcee off.

SCRAPLETS

These nasty little robotic bugs are no threat to humans, but they send robots running for their lives! They look cute until they spy metal and then it's scary-jaws time! They especially like living metal and can sense it from quite a distance.

One of the only things that will shut Scraplets down is extreme temperature, which is why they were found in the Arctic by the Autobots. Once they defrosted in Autobot HQ they soon broke out and started munching everything in sight. Cue chaos and lots of broken machinery!

When Bulkhead volunteers to be live bait to send them back via the GroundBridge, he is completely terrified. But he knows that it's the only way to save Team Prime. And it works. Just as they reach him and prepare to feast, they freeze up. Problem solved!

JaCK

Jack works at his local drive-through and lived a pretty quiet life before Arcee turned up. He still thinks he'd like a quiet life, rather than the fraught existence he has with the Autobots, but he can't seem to stay away.

His relationship with Arcee is cemented when they both face Airachnid in the jungle and he sees some of what Arcee has endured at the hands of this Decepticon. His bravery and courage during the ordeal lead to Arcee calling him 'partner', a name she won't give lightly, especially to a human.

Jack's finest moment comes when he's trapped in an old Energon mine. He manages to start up an old Energon drilling machine and drive through the rubble to help rescue Bulkhead and Miko.

STATS

AGE   15 years old.

LOCATION: Lives with his Mum.

DESCRIPTION: Ambition to own a motorcycle comes true when Arcee comes zooming into his life.

HUMAN

PROFILE

RAF

Raf is an unusual child who has an amazing ability with computers. Sometimes he can fix problems that even Ratchet can't solve. He loves Bumblebee and having a robot guardian is something he cherishes.

STATS

AGE	12 years old.
LOCATION:	Lives with his Mum and Dad.
DESCRIPTION:	Amazing ability with computers, he helps the Autobots out of many a tight spot, including helping to blow up the Decepticon Spacebridge.

As soon as he met Bumblebee he understood him straight away and they communicated easily. None of the other humans can understand Bumblebee's bleeps and blurts the way Raf can, and this makes their bond even stronger.

As the youngest in the group he's often seen as the baby, but his super-powered hacking and clever ways with computers soon show that he's not to be underestimated.

The only human to be directly attacked by Megatron, he is lucky that Ratchet guesses the cure and helps him back to life.

MIKO

Miko is the most enthusiastic of all the humans. She doesn't seem to realize how much danger she could be putting herself in, but she shows tremendous courage, even telling Bulkhead to hold a Decepticon down while she tries to bash it with a rock.

She loves having her own robot guardian, and particularly likes that Bulkhead is the muscle of the group. Her sense of fun and adventure can get her into a lot of trouble and cause some problems by distracting the Autobots too.

She's not a fan of school but manages to scrape through and lives for her time at HQ. This is where she plays video games with Jack and makes everyone play in her punk-metal band.

Her home country is Japan where her parents live and she stays with her host family in Jasper, Nevada. She makes little secret of the fact that she finds life in Jasper pretty dull and that the Autobots are the best thing to have happened to her for ages.

STATS

AGE   14 years old.

LOCATION: Staying with host family in Jasper, Nevada, her home country is Japan.

DESCRIPTION: Punk-like image with lots of attitude and enthusiasm. Constantly taking pics on her mobile – sometimes important, mostly souvenirs!

AGENT FOWLER

Special Agent Fowler is the Autobots' designated government liaison with the outside world. He constantly threatens Optimus Prime with action from the Pentagon, but they're hollow threats since he knows the strength of the robots is far greater than humans could ever reach.

He does have reason to be grateful to the Autobots since they did rescue him from interrogation by Starscream on the Nemesis.

He also enlisted the Autobots' help on the extremely delicate mission of transporting the DINGUS (Dynamic Nuclear Generation System) and making sure that Silas and his MECHs didn't get their hands on it.

STATS

AGE	Unknown, probably mid-40s.
SKILLS:	Flies fighter-planes.
DESCRIPTION:	Slightly overweight, but still ready to serve.

SILAS & MECH

HUMAN

PROFILE

MECH are a secret terror organization, led by General Silas. They are human rather than robot, and are obsessed with the belief that whoever has the most innovative technology, will

have the power to rule the world. When they find out about the existence of the Transformers, they think they have struck gold, and will stop at nothing to learn the secrets of Cybertronian technology.

MECH HQ is mobile, moving according to where they need to be at the time. Although for a while they were based in the Kamchatka Peninsula in Russia. They prefer isolated locations, where they can plan missions and evolve their technology undisturbed.

MECH first appear on the scene when they try to ambush Agent Fowler in an attempt to steal the DINGUS (Dynamic Nuclear Generation System). With the help of the Autobots, Fowler manages to fight them off, but it alerts MECH to the existence of the Cybertronians. And so MECH project 'Chimera' is born: their goal to harness the power of living machines.

MECH cannot beat the Bots and Cons in a straight fight, so instead they play dirty. Tasering Breakdown, they take him to their secret HQ and start operating on him, to discover his mechanical secrets. Thankfully before they can learn much, he is rescued by his arch-enemy Bulkhead.

Next MECH try to capture Airachnid. She evades them, but then agrees to help MECH capture Arcee and Jack, in revenge for them destroying her spaceship. But Team Prime proves too much for Airachnid and MECH, and yet again Silas gives the order for MECH to melt away from the battle.

It remains to be seen whether MECH will reappear stronger than ever. But given their obsession with Cybertronian technology, it will surely be a matter of time . . .

VEXING VEHICONS

Those pesky Vehicons will stop at nothing to catch Arcee out. Can you see how they're chasing her round town? She's got to lose them somehow, show her the best route out.

ODD ONE OUT

Can you spot the odd ones out in the rows below?

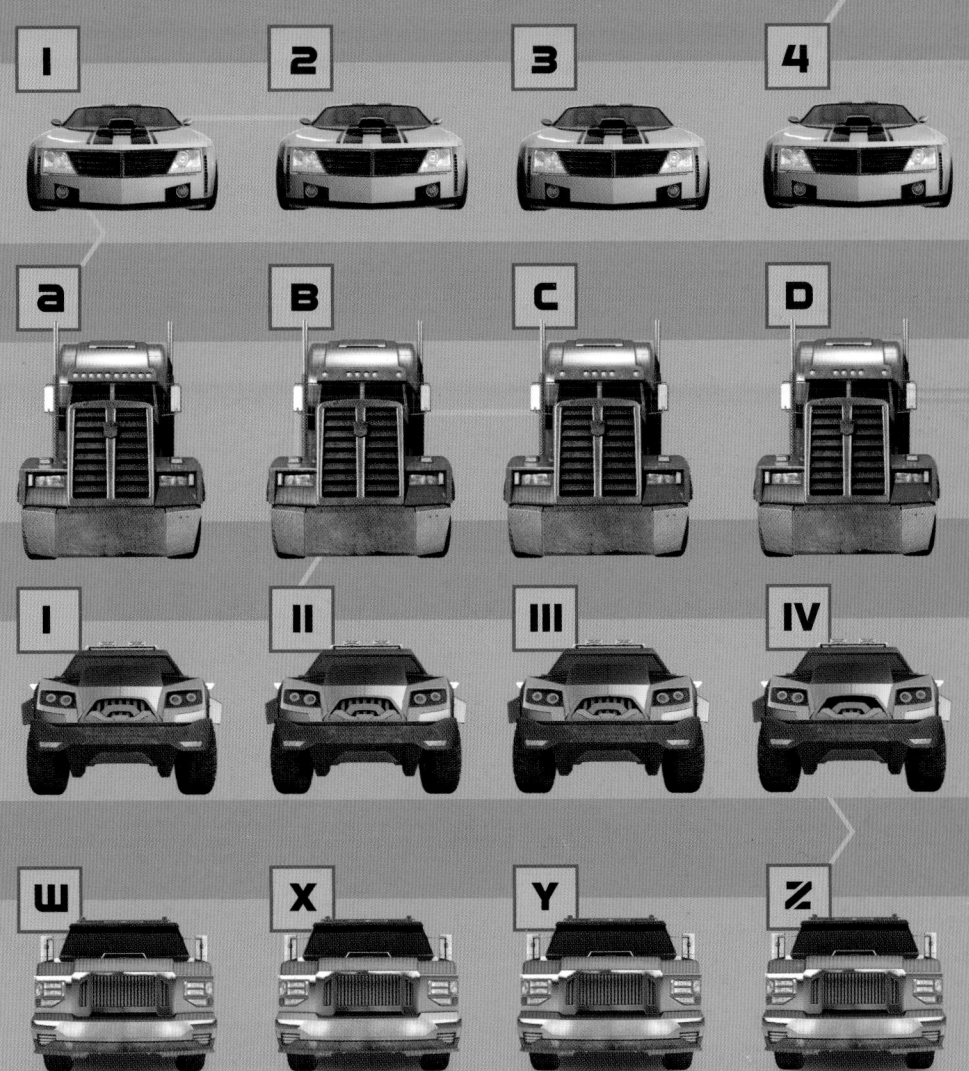

OPTIMUS PRIME

Who will eventually prevail? These two warriors have centuries of fighting behind them, and the battle is far from over.

But it was not always so. Optimus Prime was originally known as Orion Pax, when he was a data clerk in the Hall of Records on Cybertron. During this time, one of his closest friends was the gladiator turned revolutionary, Megatron. Megatron and Optimus Prime once shared the same goal, peace and freedom on Cybertron. But their vision, and means of achieving it, were vastly different.

OPTIMUS STATS

SIZE: The biggest of the Transformers.

VEHICLE MODE: Big Rig.

TEAM PRIME: Four Autobots and four humans.

VS MEGATRON

Megatron seeks peace and order through tyranny and subjugation, while Optimus Prime fights for freedom and equality.

Surprisingly, Megatron saves Optimus from dying from the Cybonic Plague, when Bumblebee persuades Megatron that he'd rather see Prime die by his own hand, than through a disease of his creation.

Optimus always hopes that one day Megatron will see the light and turn back to the Autobots, but as the centuries pass, he's beginning to realize that won't happen.

MEGATRON STATS

SIZE: An equal match to Optimus Prime.

VEHICLE MODE: Alien fighter jet.

DECEPTICON ARMY: Two lieutenants (one not so loyal), and an entire army of Troopers.

QUIZ

Are you an Autobot or a Decepticon?

1 YOU FIND A SINKHOLE OF ENERGON WHILST OUT ON PATROL. DO YOU:

A. Call for backup and your drilling drones – you'll empty the sinkhole if it's the last thing you do!

B. Call your comrades and take just what you need, others may need it someday.

2 A HUMAN GETS IN YOUR WAY DURING A HIGH-SPEED CHASE. DO YOU:

A. Crush them, worthless fleshy beings, the sooner they die out the better.

B. All life is precious, so you make sure they survive, even if it means missing an opportunity to crush the enemy.

3 YOUR LEADER IS:

A. Feared and mighty, no-one dares to cross him and any mistakes are certain to be met with punishment by death.

B. Wise, good and fair.

4 YOUR COMRADES ARE:

A. Slippery customers who are liable to stab you in the back when you're least expecting it.
B. Your best friends who will see you through anything. They make life fun and worth living.

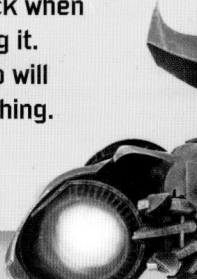

5 THE CYBONIC PLAGUE IS RAGING THROUGH THE GALAXY. DO YOU:

A. Not worry, your leader has the formula for the cure since he invented the plague in the first place. Millions will perish but not you!
B. Worry. This plague kills anyone and everyone, and as far as you know there is no cure. No-one deserves to die by it.

6 DARK ENERGON IS:

A. A valuable source of reawakening the dead to create an unstoppable army.
B. An evil thing that can never bring harmony or peace and must be destroyed.

MOSTLY As

You're a Decepticon through and through! No Autobot would want to run into you. You have no respect for life, human or otherwise, your only dream is to see Decepticons rule the skies.

MOSTLY Bs

You're proud to call yourself an Autobot! You respect all life, robotic or otherwise, and value the contact you have with any living thing.

WHO'S IN COMBAT?

Optimus and this Transformer always end up locked in bitter combat. Can you see who it is? Cross out all the letters that appear twice or more in the grid to reveal the missing word.

M	W	P	E	G
I	X	A	H	T
B	S	W	P	S
W	R	K	B	K
O	H	I	X	N

_ _ _ _ _ _ _ _

IN THE SKIES

The Decepticons have multiplied! Can you count how many there are before they take over the skies?

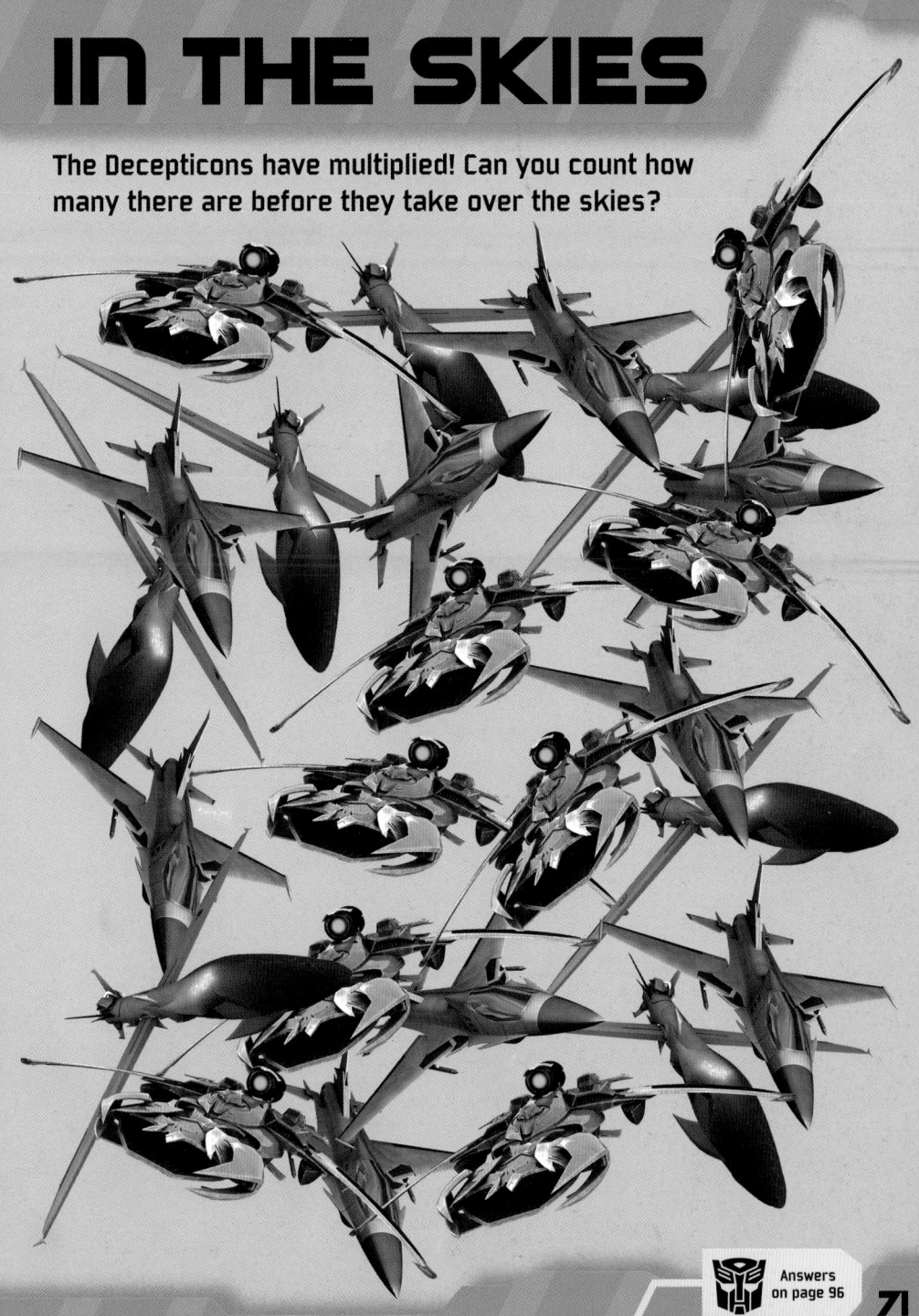

Answers on page 96

BUMBLEBEE VS

They both rely on borrowed and broken sounds to communicate, but when it comes to personality Bumblebee and Soundwave could not be more different. Both have served as scouts and advance personnel for their leaders, but where Bumblebee is curious and kind, Soundwave is vicious and cruel.

However, it would be a mistake to confuse Bumblebee's gentle nature with weakness. He is always at the front of any battle and wouldn't hesitate to take on Soundwave one to one.

BUMBLEBEE STATS

ROLE: Scout.

VEHICLE MODE: Muscle car.

SPECIAL FEATURE: Stingers.

SOUNDWAVE

Bumblebee is friendly and fun and loves being around humans and his Autobot comrades. Soundwave is a loner and would rather record conversations than have one. But one thing they have in common, as well as their methods of communication, is their total loyalty to their leaders. They would never betray them and serve their leaders loyally.

SOUNDWAVE STATS

ROLE: Scout.

VEHICLE MODE: Stealth Drone.

SPECIAL FEATURE: Laserbeak, his flying insignia which can go wherever he wills it.

BY THE ALLSPARK CONTINUED . . .

Surveying the museum, all seems quiet. The kids are transported in to get the Energon Harvester.

But Decepticons Knockout and Breakdown aren't far behind them, and they don't care about keeping undercover.

The kids nearly manage to get the Harvester cleanly away.

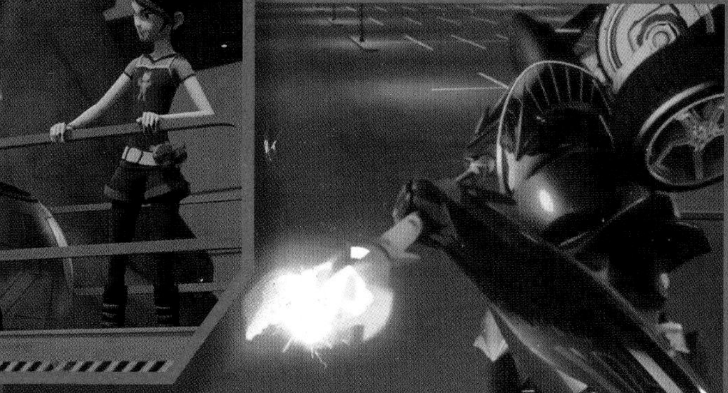

But they are only human, how can they compete with the Decepticons?

And the story continues . . .

CROSSWORD

ACROSS

1. The muscle of the Autobots

4. Human girl who wishes she was a robot!

6. Autobot who changes into a motorbike

8. Short name for a Decepticon

9. Raf is _ _ _ _ by Megatron when he fires at Bumblebee

10. The Destroyer – Dark Energon runs in his blood

DOWN

1. Black and yellow markings are his distinctive style

2. Scary spider Decepticon

3. Leader of the Decepticons

5. The medic of the Decepticons

7. Lifesource and fuel for all Transformers

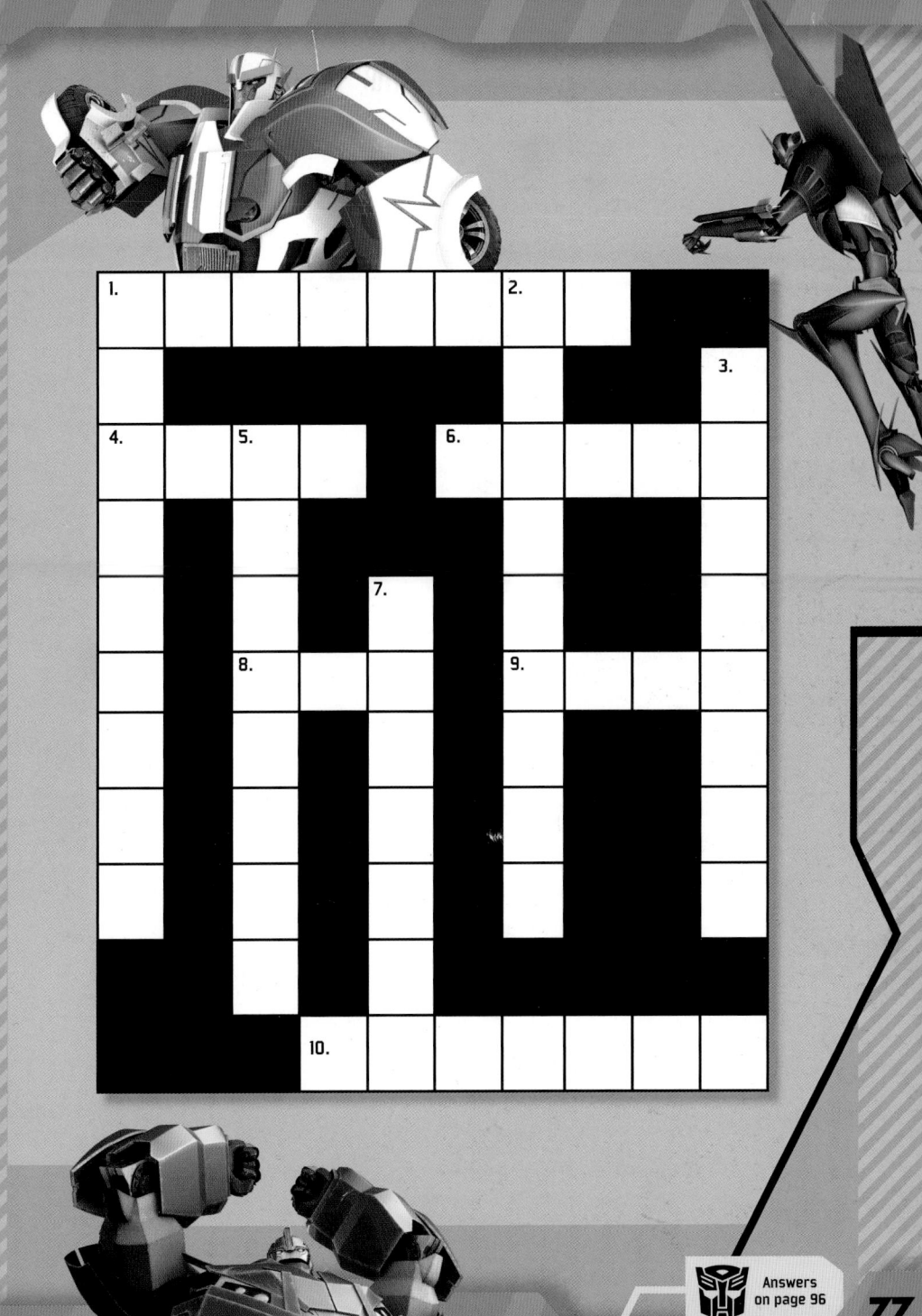

Answers on page 96

ARCEE VS

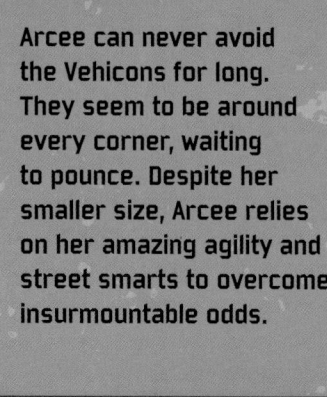

Arcee can never avoid
the Vehicons for long.
They seem to be around
every corner, waiting
to pounce. Despite her
smaller size, Arcee relies
on her amazing agility and
street smarts to overcome
insurmountable odds.

ARCEE STATS

SPEED: 110mph.

VEHICLE MODE: Motorbike.

VULNERABILITY: Vehicons know she will risk
her own safety to protect
Jack and all humans.

VEHICONS

The Vehicons are always around when Arcee is doing her best to protect Jack. They sense that she cares deeply for him and know that it's the best chink in her armour.

But Arcee can normally rely on one of her trusty sidekicks to come to her rescue. It's just sometimes they take a bit longer than she would like.

VEHICON STATS

SPEED: 110mph.

VEHICLE MODE: Sedan car.

VULNERABILITY: Being recalled on a whim by Starscream.

GROUNDBRIDGE

The GroundBridge is used by the Autobots and was invented by Ratchet to help them navigate their way quickly and easily around Earth.

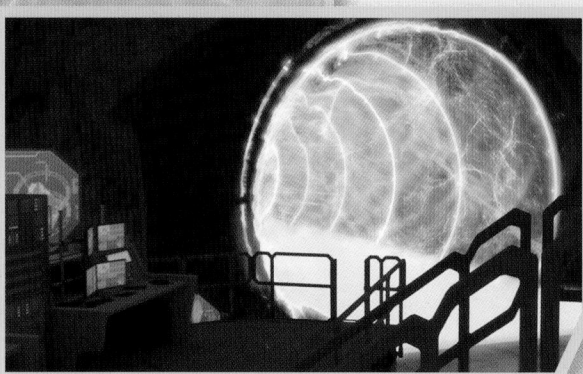

Ratchet based the design of the GroundBridge on the Spacebridge. It only works if someone is able to operate it from Autobot HQ.

GROUNDBRIDGE

USED BY: Secret weapon of the Autobots.

DISTANCE COVERED: Can transport Team Prime anywhere on Earth. Technically it's not meant to reach space, although the Autobots risked it to blow up the Spacebridge.

DAMAGE SUSTAINED: It was broken by the Scraplets, but Ratchet managed to repair it.

VS SPACEBRIDGE

The Spacebridge was commandeered by the Decepticons and used by Megatron for his triumphant return. They were able to travel anywhere in the galaxy with it. Megatron's plan was to use the Spacebridge to transport the Terrorcons from Cybertron to Earth.

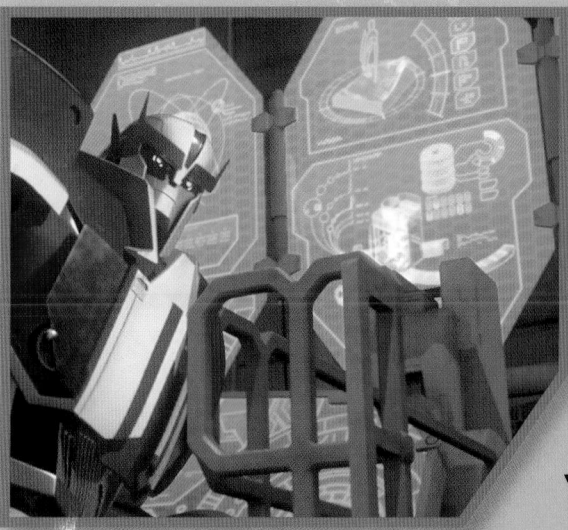

The Autobots managed to blow up the Spacebridge when they realized what Megatron was planning. Ratchet was able to advise Arcee and Bumblebee how to reverse the flow of Energon so the Spacebridge imploded.

SPACEBRIDGE

USED BY: Commandeered by Decepticons after leaving Cybertron.

DISTANCE COVERED: Intergalactic travel – anywhere in space.

DAMAGE SUSTAINED: Blown up by the Autobots, its current status remains uncertain.

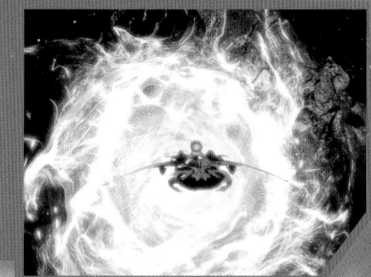

CYBERTRONIAN SECRETS

Cybertron has many ancient secrets. Whenever one of them is revealed, it's a race between the Autobots and the Decepticons to find it as soon as possible.

THE ENERGON HARVESTER

DISCOVERED BY: Breakdown, and soon after by Bulkhead and Miko.

FUNCTION: To harvest Energon from any source, especially other Bots and Cons.

FATE: Destroyed by the Autobots.

THE POLARITY GAUNTLET

DISCOVERED BY: Megatron sends Breakdown to retrieve it, but Airachnid and Arcee and Bulkhead follow hot on his heels.

FUNCTION: A Decepticon invention that can magnetize other Bots and Cons to each other.

FATE: The Autobots take it back to their HQ.

CYBERTRONIAN SECRETS

THE IMMOBILIZER

DISCOVERED BY: Airachnid and Starscream go to retrieve it from the crash site of a Decepticon ship, but the Autobots soon turn up.

FUNCTION: As soon as it is fired at a Bot it immobilizes them.

FATE: Airachnid thinks it's broken, but the Autobots take it back to HQ where it is repaired by Ratchet.

CYBERTRONIAN DATA CYLINDER

DISCOVERED BY: The Decepticons, but the Autobots are hot on their trail and have an uninvited hitchhiker along for the ride – Miko! She tries to get the cylinder when battle is raging, but it senses a foreign body and shoots its data straight into the air and into Bulkhead!

FUNCTION: To contain information, sometimes history, sometimes formulas. In this case it holds the formula to synthetic Energon.

FATE: The empty cylinder is crushed by Megatron. Bulkhead gives the formula to the Autobots, but comes scarily close to losing his mind.

BULKHEAD VS

This is the ultimate match of sheer force against blistering speed. Bulkhead is the bull in the china shop, while Starscream could thread a needle at Mach 4.

But what Bulkhead lacks in finesse, he more than makes up for in heart. Few Autobots are more dedicated to the cause, and Bulkhead would trade blows with Starscream any day. If he could just get his hands on him.

BULKHEAD STATS

ROLE: Muscle man.

VEHICLE MODE: All Terrain Vehicle.

VULNERABILITY: Can be clumsy.

STARSCREAM

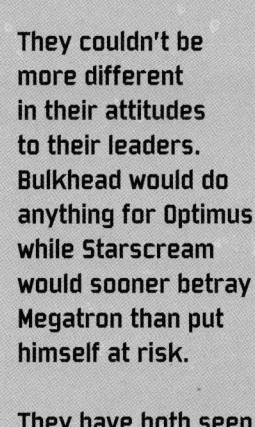

They couldn't be more different in their attitudes to their leaders. Bulkhead would do anything for Optimus while Starscream would sooner betray Megatron than put himself at risk.

They have both seen centuries of war and are skilled fighters and seasoned warriors. But who would win in Bot to Con combat?

STARSCREAM STATS

ROLE: Deceiver.

VEHICLE MODE: Military Fighter Jet.

VULNERABILITY: Always prefers the sneaky approach.

All is lost and Miko gets arrested! But she's soon busted out.

And then a fresh signal comes through . . . the Decepticons are playing with their new toy!

The Autobots can track the Harvester's signal, leading them straight to the Cons.

Bulkhead battles Starscream. Even with Energon leaching out of him, he manages to grab the Harvester and crush it. Breaking things is his speciality!

THE END

ENERGON MAZE

Can you make your way through the maze and reach the
Energon Harvester before the Decepticons steal it?

CRACK THE CODE

Can you work out what each letter has been switched for and see what message Fowler has left for the Autobots.

A	B	C	D	E	F	G	H	I	J	K	L	M
F			I				M				Q	

N	O	P	Q	R	S	T	U	V	W	X	Y	Z
		V				Z	A					

The Y D I B P N is a

————————

Y T I V H D X   I P X G Z V M

———————— ————————

B Z I Z M V O D J I   N T N O Z H

———————— ————————

Answers on page 96

OPTIMUS PRIME

'When the hundred spheres align, a perpetual conflict will culminate upon a world forged from Chaos, and the weak shall perish in the shadow of a Rising Darkness.'

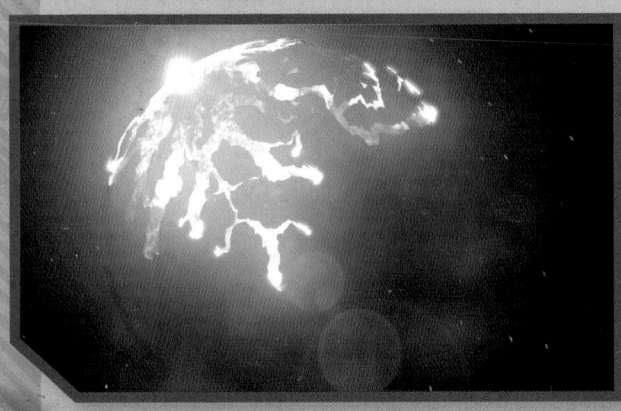

The power of Dark Energon has drawn Megatron to an ancient Cybertronian prophecy called the Covenant of Primus. Ratchet explains that many centuries ago on Cybertron, Primus and the original thirteen Primes banished Unicron the Destroyer from their planet. But Team Prime realize that, as the Chaos Bringer drifted through space, he formed with various minerals to become planet Earth, filling its core with Dark Energon.

VS UNICRON

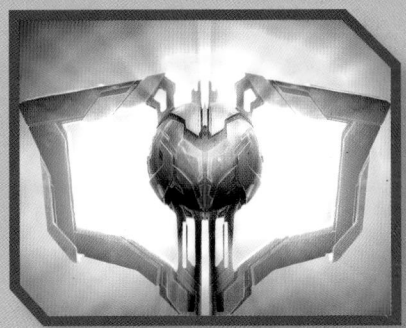

As the planetary alignment described in the prophecy forms around Earth, it starts to bring Unicron out of his slumber. Megatron tries pledging his loyalty to Unicron, but he is refused. Angry that Megatron has not rid the Earth of Optimus, the last of the Primes, Unicron decides to battle the Autobot leader himself.

Optimus is the only one who can defeat Unicron, since he has the secret of the Primes deep within him, the Matrix of Leadership. Ratchet explains that the honour of becoming a Prime can only be achieved through earning the Matrix, deep inside the core of Cyberton. This was how Orion Pax became Optimus, the last of the Primes.

But Optimus cannot defeat Unicron alone. He needs guidance, and Megatron is the only one able to lead him to Unicron's spark chamber, hidden deep in Earth's core. Megatron, furious at being rejected by Unicron, is now desperate to be rid of the Destroyer. He knows that Unicron has no intention of forming an alliance with him, and once fully awakened, he will be unstoppable. So Optimus and Megatron form an unlikely truce. The Autobots don't like it one bit. But they recognize that to save the Earth, they may just have to rely on Megatron.

To reach Unicron's spark chamber, they use the GroundBridge and coordinates supplied by Megatron. But Megatron is being affected by the Dark Energon, and he realizes that Unicron is trying to control him. Once the team is deep within the Earth's core, Unicron starts to bend Megatron's mind. Unicron orders him to kill Optimus, but Megatron manages to throw him off. At last, Optimus manages to pour the Matrix of Leadership into Unicron.

It is done! Unicron is defeated. But Optimus lies helpless, drained of all energy. Megatron stands over him, ready to finish him off. But then Optimus stirs, and calls him by his old name, 'Megatronus'. Ratchet realizes that when Optimus gave up the Matrix, he lost more than just the wisdom of the Primes, he lost his own memories.

Megatron understands this, and that Optimus believes himself to be Orion Pax. In Optimus's mind they are friends, and he has no memories of the Great War between the Bots and the Cons. Megatron tells Optimus that the two of them are under attack from enemy Autobots, and that they need to retreat to their Decepticon ship.

Will Optimus Prime become a Decepticon?

TRANSFORMERS WORDSEARCH

Is your Transformer knowledge up to scratch?
Find out by locating these characters hidden in the
square. You'll need extra Energon to complete it!

A	U	T	O	B	O	T	S	W	I
V	S	U	M	I	T	P	O	H	N
E	D	A	E	H	K	L	U	B	O
H	O	Z	R	C	S	O	N	E	R
I	L	U	A	C	K	Q	D	N	T
C	I	J	F	I	E	E	W	R	A
O	S	P	M	E	N	E	A	G	G
N	E	M	E	S	I	S	V	O	E
S	T	A	R	S	C	R	E	A	M
B	E	E	B	E	L	B	M	U	B

AUTOBOTS

OPTIMUS

BUMBLEBEE

ARCEE

BULKHEAD

MEGATRON

STARSCREAM

SOUNDWAVE

JACK

MIKO

RAF

VEHICONS

NEMESIS

Answers
on page 96

95

answers

PAGE 18 – STEALTHY CHARACTERS
A – 2, B – 1, C – 3

PAGE 22 – DECEPTICON ALERT!

PAGE 23 – ENERGON CRISIS

			■	E	N	E	R	G	0
P	H	S	W	P	U	T	I	E	N
N	O	G	R	E	N	E	Z	N	E
E	E	C	F	Y	H	N	O	G	R
N	U	K	M	A	V	T	P	I	A
E	R	G	O	N	S	R	G	O	L
M	U	T	P	E	N	E	Z	N	Z
N	X	B	C	D	V	X	N	E	Q
E	R	G	N	O	G	R	E	Q	E
A	V	O	E	N	E	R	G	X	X
J	X	I	G	N	E	N	O	P	F
D	S	C	R	G	O	N			→

PAGE 26 – WHO'S OUT OF THE FRAME?
D

PAGE 27 – SPACE EQUATION
Message reads: SPACEBRIDGE TO CYBERTRON.

PAGE 30 – TRUE OR FALSE?
1 – TRUE, 2 – FALSE, 3 – TRUE, 4 – FALSE, 5 – FALSE.

PAGE 31 – WORD GAME
Hidden command: ROLLOUT

R O A <u>R</u> I D E

S I L <u>O</u> P E N

W A L <u>L</u> E A D

H I L <u>L</u> O O K

A L S <u>O</u> V E R

Y O <u>U</u> N I T

T E N <u>T</u> H A T

PAGE 40 – AUTOBOT FIT

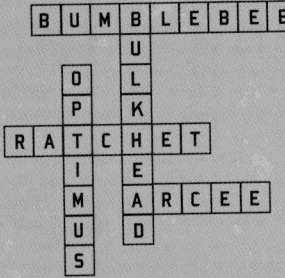

PAGE 44 – WHO'S THIS?
1 – BULKHEAD, 2 – OPTIMUS, 3 – ARCEE, 4- STARSCREAM, 5 – JACK, 6 – RAF, 7 – SOUNDWAVE.

PAGE 64 – VEXING VEHICONS

PAGE 65 – ODD ONE OUT
Bumblebee – 3, Optimus – A, Bulkhead – IV, Ratchet – X.

PAGE 70 – WHO'S IN COMBAT?
MEGATRON

PAGE 71 – IN THE SKIES
25 Decepticons

PAGE 76 – CROSSWORD

PAGE 90 – ENERGON MAZE

PAGE 91 – CRACK THE CODE

A	B	C	D	E	F	G	H	I	J	K	L	M
F	G	H	I	J	K	L	M	N	O	P	Q	R

N	O	P	Q	R	S	T	U	V	W	X	Y	Z
S	T	U	V	W	X	Y	Z	A	B	C	D	E

Message reads: The DINGUS is a DYNAMIC NUCLEAR GENERATION SYSTEM.

PAGE 95 – WORDSEARCH

A	U	T	O	B	O	T	S	W	I
Y	S	U	M	I	T	P	O	H	N
E	D	A	E	H	K	L	U	B	O
H	O	Z	A	E	S	O	N	E	R
	L	U	K	O	O	D	N	T
C	I	J	F	E	E	W	R	A
O	S	P	M	E	N	E	A	G	G
N	E	M	E	S	I	S	V	O	E
S	T	A	R	S	C	R	E	A	M
B	E	E	B	E	L	B	M	U	B